Licensed exclusively to Top That Publishing Ltd
Tide Mill Way, Woodbridge, Suffolk, IP12 1AP, UK
www.topthatpublishing.com
Copyright © 2016 Tide Mill Media
All rights reserved
0 2 4 6 8 9 7 5 3 1
Manufactured in China

Written by Oakley Graham
Illustrated by Patricia Yuste

ISBN 978-1-78700-009-4

A catalogue record for this book is available from the British Library

When I dream of Christmas

Written by Oakley Graham

Illustrated by Patricia Yuste

Elves

Elves work all year long making toys for good girls and boys. Despite their small size, elves' most favourite thing to do is play basketball with Father Christmas.

Christmas Trees

Christmas trees are happiest when they are dressed in glittering lights and baubles. Always put a Christmas tree close to a window so they can see their friends outside.

Reindeer

Reindeer don't receive many Christmas cards as their names are very difficult to spell. Despite this, they are not at all grumpy and help Father Christmas to pull his sleigh.

Donner

Rudolph

Blitzen

Angels

Angels look a bit like a baby brother
or sister, but they do not wear nappies.
Angels enjoy singing Christmas carols
and meeting up with their friends
at old churches.

Carol Singers

Carol singers have big, red smiley faces and like to sing jolly Christmas songs at the top of their voices. Despite the name, you do not have to be called Carol to be a carol singer.

Stockings

Always hang out a stocking for Father Christmas on Christmas Eve. Never hang out dirty socks as this is considered quite rude and can make your presents smell like cheese.

Presents

Presents are a fantastic Christmas invention. It is recommended that you only open presents if they are addressed to you, as opening other people's can make them rather sad.

Father Christmas

Father Christmas lives at the
North Pole with the elves and is nearly
always laughing or telling jokes.
Father Christmas's favourite colour is red,
and he is never ever grumpy.

Shepherds

Shepherds live on hills and like to race their sheep very late at night. They always warm their smelly socks over an open fire and love eating trifle.

Wise Men

Wise men are very, very clever,

and always give expensive presents.

They love to answer difficult questions,

but are not allowed to appear on

game shows.

The North Pole

The North Pole is a magical place where Father Christmas and his elves live. Although the North Pole is very cold, they keep warm by eating lots of toasted marshmallows and drinking hot chocolate.

The Baby Jesus

When I dream of Christmas, I dream
about the baby Jesus wrapped up
in a manger, who would grow up
to be our saviour.

Merry Christmas!